Contents

Seven for a Secret

Doing the Don'ting

Quick as a Lick

Up Tails All

Seven for a Secret

In this section there are rhymes about the days of the week and the letters of the alphabet, rhymes to say when counting magpies, and rhymes about church bells. You probably know some of them already.

Black Friars

Seven Black Friars,
Sitting back to back,
Fished from the bridge
For a pike or a jack.
The first caught a tiddler,
The second caught a crab,
The third caught a winkle,
The fourth caught a dab,
The fifth caught a tadpole,
The sixth caught an eel,
And the seventh caught
An old cart-wheel.

Eleanor Farjeon

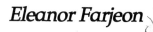

Magpies

One for sorrow, two for joy,
Three for a wedding, four for a boy,
Five for silver, six for gold,
Seven for a secret, never to be told.

Anon.

Sneeze on Monday

Sneeze on Monday, sneeze for danger,
Sneeze on Tuesday, meet a stranger,
Sneeze on Wednesday, sneeze for a letter,
Sneeze on Thursday, something better,
Sneeze on Friday, sneeze for sorrow,
Sneeze on Saturday, see your sweetheart tomorrow.

Anon.

Monday's Child

Monday's child is fair of face,
Tuesday's child is full of grace,
Wednesday's child is full of woe,
Thursday's child has far to go,
Friday's child is loving and giving,
Saturday's child works hard for a living,
But the child that is born on the Sabbath day
Is bonny and blithe and good and gay.

Anon.

The Wolf's Rhyme

Monday's child is fairly tough,
Tuesday's child is tender enough,
Wednesday's child is good to fry,
Thursday's child is best in pie,
Friday's child makes good meat roll,
Saturday's child is casserole,
But the child that is born on the Sabbath day
Is delicious when eaten in any way.

Catherine Storr,
from *Clever Polly and the Stupid Wolf*

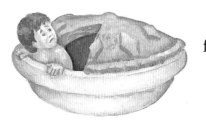

4

Solomon Grundy

Solomon Grundy, born on Monday,
Christened on Tuesday, married on Wednesday,
Took ill on Thursday, worse on Friday,
Died on Saturday, buried on Sunday,
That was the end of Solomon Grundy.

Anon.

The Bells of Northampton

Roast beef and marshmallows,
Say the bells of All Hallows';
Pancakes and fritters,
Say the bells of St Peter's;
Roast beef and boiled,
Say the bells of St Giles';
Poker and tongs,
Say the bells of St John's.

Anon.

A for Alice

A for Alice who climbed a tree,

B for Ben who caught a flea,

C for Carol, playing a trick,

D for Dennis who was awfully sick,

E for Errol, out to play,

F for Fiona who ran away,

G for Gemma, making bread,

H for Hiroko, under the bed,

I for Ian, flying his kite,

J for Jamal, engaged in a fight,

K for Kate, who came in late,

L for Laura who thinks she's great,

M for Maria who's always good,

N for Nick, never does what he should,

O for Oliver, in a muddle,

P for Paul who sat down in a puddle,

Q for Queenie, jumping the rope,

R for Rosy who wants to be pope,

S for Shazeia who wins the race,

T for Tracey, making a face,

U for Una, trying to smile,

V for Vijay, dressing in style,

W for Wendy, building a house,

X for Xavier, afraid of a mouse,

Y for Yael who loves to tease,

Z for Zadok who prays on his knees.

June O'Watt

W

The king he sent for his wise men all
To find a rhyme for W;
When they had thought a good long time
But could not think of a single rhyme,
"I'm sorry," said he, "to trouble you."

James Reeves

Apple-pie

A was an Apple-pie.

B bit it, C cut it, D dealt it,

E enjoyed it, F fought for it,

G got it, H hoped for it,

I inquired about it,

J jumped on it, K kept it,

L longed for it, M mourned for it,

N nodded at it, O opened it,

P peeped in it, Q quartered it,

R ran for it, S sat on it, T took it,

U upset it, V viewed it, W wanted it,

X crossed it, Y yearned for it,

And Z put it in his pocket, and said,

"Well done!"

Anon.

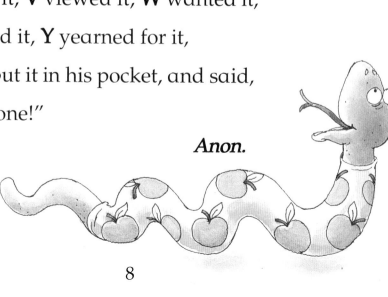

1. Do you know any counting rhymes? Perhaps you say them in the playground. Tell each other some of your rhymes. How many different ones can your class remember?

2. You can write a new rhyme for the days of the week, like the one by Catherine Storr.
Go through the week saying what clothes each child wears. For example:
Monday's child wears a hat on her head,
Tuesday's child wears pyjamas in bed ...

3. Work with a friend and see if you can make up your own alphabet of animals, people or things. For example:
A was an ant who crawled up the wall, B was a ...
A is an aunt who always kisses me, B is a ...
A for an arrow that flies through the air, B for a ...
Don't worry about rhyming, but, if you can, do.

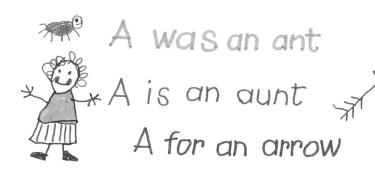

Doing the Don'ting

Do you recognise yourself in any of these poems?

The Muddy Puddle

I am sitting
In the middle
Of a rather Muddy
Puddle,
With my bottom
Full of bubbles
And my rubbers
Full of Mud,

And I find that
What a person
With a puddle
Round his middle
Thinks of mostly
In the muddle
Is the Muddi-
Ness of Mud.

Dennis Lee

While my jacket
And my sweater
Go on slowly
Getting wetter
As I very
Slowly settle
To the Bottom
Of the Mud.

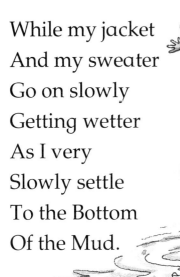

Wizard

Under my bed I keep a box
With seven locks,

And all the things I have to hide
Are safe inside:

My rings, my wand, my hat, my shells,
My book of spells.

I could fit a mountain into a shoe
If I wanted to,

Or put the sea in a paper cup
And drink it up.

I could change a cushion into a bird
With a magic word,

Or turn December into spring,
Or make stones sing.

I could clap my hands and watch the moon,
Like a white balloon,

Come floating to my window-sill ...
One day I will.

Richard Edwards

Don't

Why do people say "don't" so much,
Whenever you try something new?
It's more fun doing the don'ting,
So why don't people say "do"?

Don't slurp your spaghetti
Don't kiss the cat
Don't butter your fingers
Don't walk like that
Don't wash your books
Don't bubble your tea
Don't jump on your sister
Don't goggle at me
Don't climb up the curtains
Don't feed the chair
Don't sleep in your wardrobe
Don't cut off your hair
Don't draw on the pillow
Don't change all the clocks
Don't water the phone

Don't hide my socks
Don't cycle upstairs
Don't write on the eggs
Don't chew your pyjamas
Don't paint your legs ...

Oh, why do people say "don't" so much,
When ever you try something new?
It's more fun doing the don'ting,
So why don't people say "do"?

Richard Edwards

This is the Hand

This is the hand
that touched the frost
that froze my tongue
and made it numb

this is the hand
that cracked the nut
that went in my mouth
and never came out

this is the hand
that slid round the bath
to find the soap
that wouldn't float

this is the hand
on the hot water bottle
meant to warm my bed
that got lost instead

this is the hand
that held the bottle
that let go of the soap
that cracked the nut
that touched the frost
this is the hand
that never gets lost.

Michael Rosen

The End

When I was One,
I had just begun.

When I was Two,
I was nearly new.

When I was Three,
I was hardly me.

When I was Four,
I was not much more.

When I was Five,
I was just alive.

But now I am Six, I'm as clever as clever.
So I think I'll be six now for ever and ever.

A. A. Milne

The Radio Men

When I was little more than six
I thought that men must be
Alive inside the radio
To act in plays, or simply blow
Trumpets, or sing to me.

I never got a glimpse of them,
They were so very small.
But I imagined them in there,
Their voices bursting on the air
Through that thin, wooden wall.

Elizabeth Jennings

1. Make a list of all the things that people tell you *not* to do. You might also try to list all the things people say you *should* do; for example,
***Do* wash behind your ears ...**
You could then make a poem using ideas from both lists.

2. Michael Rosen wrote about his hand. What about *your* hand, or foot? For example:
This is the foot that trod on the sand
That washed on the beach when the sea came in ...
As you write, say the words out loud and hear the rhythm.

Quick as a Lick

Here you will find rhymes and poems that use **alliteration** – you might call them tongue-twisters. Alliteration is when the same sound is repeated, usually at the beginning of words. It is fun to try to say some of the rhymes fast. Try saying the first two as quickly as you can.

Swan Swam

Swan swam over the sea – swim, swan, swim.
Swan swam back again – well swum, swan.

Anon.

She Sells Sea-shells

She sells sea-shells on the sea shore,
The shells she sells are sea-shells I'm sure.
So, if she sells sea-shells on the sea shore,
Then I'm sure she sells sea-shore shells.

Anon.

The next two poems use alliteration too, but are not meant to be tongue-twisters.

One Wet Wellington

One wet wellington walked on water,
Two tired travellers tried to talk,
Three thin thinkers went to the theatre,
Four foolish fishermen fished with a fork,
Five frozen fingers felt for the fire,
Six sorry sinners sat full of sad sighs,
Seven solemn secrets could softly inspire,
Eight electric eels with enormous eyes,
Nine new nestlings, none of them yet named,
Ten tailless tabby cats, truly tamed.

Eva Rupp

18

Freddie Phipps

Freddie Phipps
Liked fish and chips.
Jesse Pinch liked crime.

Woodrow Waters
Liked dollars and quarters.
Paul Small liked a dime.

Sammy Fink
Liked a lemon drink.
Jeremy Jones liked lime.

Mortimer Mills
Liked running down hills.
Jack Jay liked to climb.

Hamilton Hope
Liked water and soap.
Georgie Green liked grime;

But Willy Earls
Liked pretty girls
And had a much better time.

Charles Causley

19

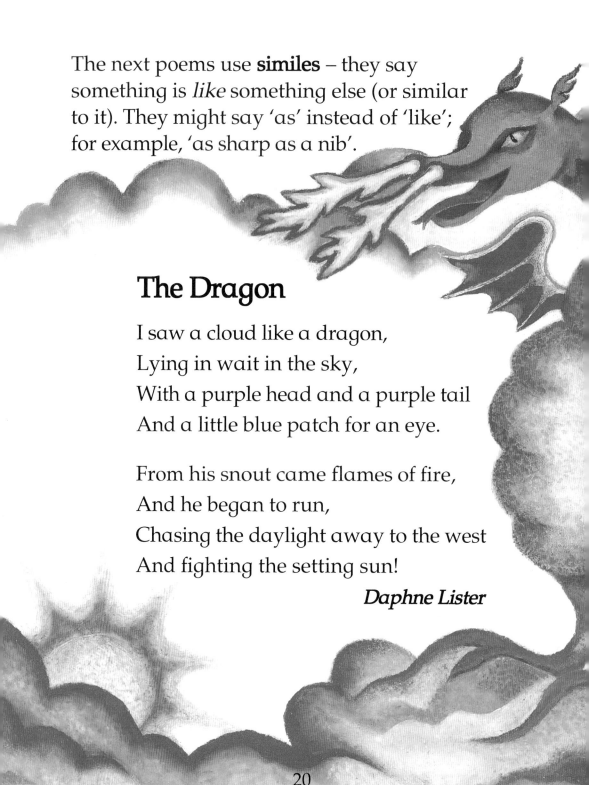

The next poems use **similes** – they say something is *like* something else (or similar to it). They might say 'as' instead of 'like'; for example, 'as sharp as a nib'.

The Dragon

I saw a cloud like a dragon,
Lying in wait in the sky,
With a purple head and a purple tail
And a little blue patch for an eye.

From his snout came flames of fire,
And he began to run,
Chasing the daylight away to the west
And fighting the setting sun!

Daphne Lister

The Writer of this Poem

The writer of this poem
Is taller than a tree
As keen as the North Wind
As handsome as can be

As bold as a boxing-glove
As sharp as a nib
As strong as scaffolding
As tricky as a fib

As smooth as a lolly-ice
As quick as a lick
As clean as a chemist-shop
As clever as a ✔

The writer of this poem
Never ceases to amaze
He's one in a million billion
(or so the poem says!)

Roger McGough

Cow

The cow
Coming
Across the grass
Moves
Like a mountain
Towards us;
Her hipbones
Jut
Like sharp
Peaks
Of stone,
Her hoofs
Thump
Like dropped
Rocks:
Almost
Too late
She stops.

Valerie Worth

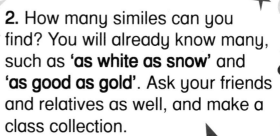

I. Make up some tongue-twisters with a friend and ask other people if they can say them. If you look in the dictionary you will find lots of words that begin with the same letter. You can use some of these for your tongue-twister.

2. How many similes can you find? You will already know many, such as **'as white as snow'** and **'as good as gold'**. Ask your friends and relatives as well, and make a class collection.

Up Tails All

There have been so many poems written about animals of all sizes – from the microbe to the elephant and the dinosaur. This selection of animal poems starts with a poem about badgers.

Badgers

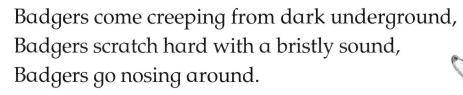

Badgers come creeping from dark underground,
Badgers scratch hard with a bristly sound,
Badgers go nosing around.

Badgers have whiskers and black and white faces,
Badger cubs scramble and scrap and run races,
Badgers like overgrown places.

Badgers don't jump when a vixen screams,
Badgers drink quietly from moonshiny streams,
Badgers dig holes in our dreams.

Badgers are working while you and I sleep,
Pushing their tunnels down twisting and steep,
Badgers have secrets to keep.

Richard Edwards

Jim-Jam Pyjamas

He wears striped jim-jam pyjamas,
You never saw jim-jams like those –
A fine-fitting, stretchy, fur cat-suit,
Skin-tight from his head to his toes.

He wears striped jim-jam pyjamas,
Black and yellow and dashingly gay;
He makes certain that everyone sees them
By keeping them on all the day.

He wears striped jim-jam pyjamas,
He walks with a smug-pussy stride;
There's no hiding his pride in his jim-jams
With their zig-zaggy lines down each side.

He wears striped jim-jam pyjamas
And pauses at times to display
The effect as he flexes his torso –
Then he fancies he hears people say:

"I wish I had jim-jam pyjamas!
I wish I were feline and slim!
Oh, look at that brave Bengal tiger!
Oh, how I should love to be him!"

Gina Wilson

Cat's Funeral

Bury her deep, down deep,
Safe in the earth's cold keep,
Bury her deep –

No more to watch bird stir;
No more to clean dark fur;
No more to glisten as silk;
No more to revel in milk;
No more to purr.

Bury her deep, down deep;
She is beyond warm sleep.
She will not walk in the night;
She will not wake to the light.
Bury her deep.

E. V. Rieu

Seal Lullaby

Oh! hush thee, my baby, the night is behind us,
And black are the waters that sparkled so green.
The moon, o'er the combers*, looks downward to find us
At rest in the hollows that rustle between.
Where billow meets billow, there soft be thy pillow;
Ah, weary wee flipperling, curl at thy ease!
The storm shall not wake thee, nor sharks overtake thee,
Asleep in the arms of the slow-swinging seas.

Rudyard Kipling

(* Combers are waves.)

The Owl and the Pussy-Cat

The Owl and the Pussy-Cat went to sea
In a beautiful pea-green boat,
They took some honey, and plenty of money
Wrapped up in a five-pound note.
The Owl looked up to the stars above,
And sang to a small guitar,
"O lovely Pussy, O Pussy, my love,
What a beautiful Pussy you are,
You are,
You are!
What a beautiful Pussy you are!"

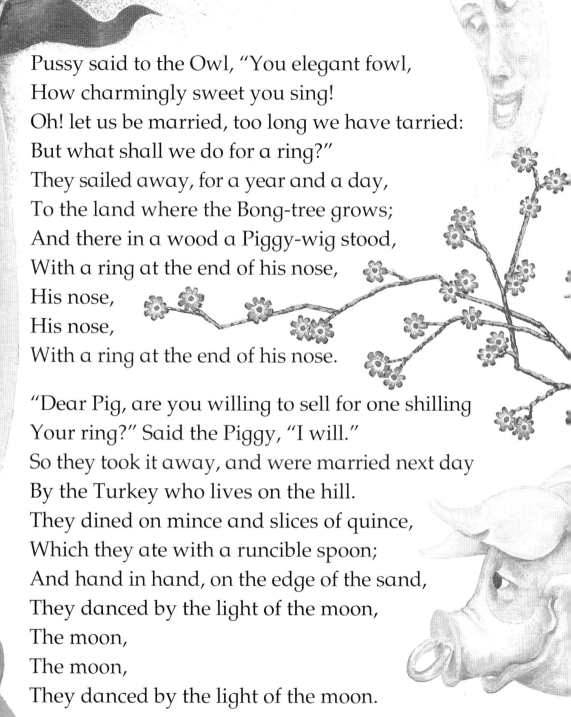

Pussy said to the Owl, "You elegant fowl,
How charmingly sweet you sing!
Oh! let us be married, too long we have tarried:
But what shall we do for a ring?"
They sailed away, for a year and a day,
To the land where the Bong-tree grows;
And there in a wood a Piggy-wig stood,
With a ring at the end of his nose,
His nose,
His nose,
With a ring at the end of his nose.

"Dear Pig, are you willing to sell for one shilling
Your ring?" Said the Piggy, "I will."
So they took it away, and were married next day
By the Turkey who lives on the hill.
They dined on mince and slices of quince,
Which they ate with a runcible spoon;
And hand in hand, on the edge of the sand,
They danced by the light of the moon,
The moon,
The moon,
They danced by the light of the moon.

Edward Lear

Ducks' Ditty

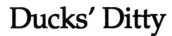

All along the backwater,
Through the rushes tall,
Ducks are a-dabbling,
Up tails all!

Ducks' tails, drakes' tails,
Yellow feet a-quiver,
Yellow bills all out of sight
Busy in the river!

Slushy green undergrowth
Where the roach swim –
Here we keep our larder
Cool and full and dim.

Every one for what he likes!
We like to be
Heads down, tails up,
Dabbling free!

High in the blue above
Swifts whirl and call –
We are down a-dabbling,
Up tails all!

Kenneth Grahame

The Duck

Behold the duck.
It does not cluck.
A cluck it lacks.
It quacks.
It is especially fond
Of a puddle or a pond.
When it dines or sups,
It bottoms ups.

Ogden Nash

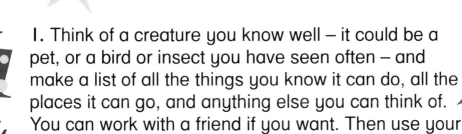

1. Think of a creature you know well – it could be a pet, or a bird or insect you have seen often – and make a list of all the things you know it can do, all the places it can go, and anything else you can think of. You can work with a friend if you want. Then use your list to write a poem about the creature.

2. If you could be any animal, what would you be, and why? What sorts of things would you look forward to doing? You could start your poem like this:
I'd like to be a ...

Index